ALPHA ANIMALS

HELEN L. ROBINSON

ALPHA ANIMALS

Written by: Helen L. Robinson
Illustrated by: Vonzell Byrd
Graphics by: Ciamino Dillon

© Copyright 2020
All rights reserved
ISBN: 978-1-949027-30-3

Destined To Publish
www.DestinedToPublish.com

DEDICATION

It is with my deepest gratitude and warmest affection that I dedicate this book to my late grandparents, Armielee and Wenners Ballard. You will forever be missed.

To my beautiful children Leah, Elijah, David, the late Leslie and the late DJ, you are the music of my heart and my inspiration.

I love you so much.
~ Mommy

ACKNOWLEDGMENTS

This book would not have been made possible without the spirit, love, and encouragement that has pushed me to move forward. Thank you, Lord Jesus, for your everlasting love. I am humbled and grateful for this opportunity.

To my parents Joanne and Albert Lewis thank you for encouraging me to "keep on writing". I did it!! I love you.

To my brother Dr. Theo Robinson – I love you.

Ciamino Dillon – Love is sustained by an action, a pattern of devotion in the things that we do every day. Thank you for being my love.

To my aunts and uncles- Wenners, Carolyn, Tina and Q, you were there when I began my writer's journey. Thank you for waking up and listening sometimes way past the midnight hour.

I love you all!

Vanetta Brown- my best friend in the whole wide world and sister in the spirit. Thank you for your love and friendship. Blood could not make us any closer.

Lisa Williams, the ladies of WILS and WOP thank you always being just a prayer away.

Vonzell Byrd thank you for bringing my words to life.

To the countless loved ones, friends, colleagues and students both past and present I love you with my whole heart. Charlene Searcy, Chelsey Robinson, Thaddeus Peyton, Kimberley Jones, Erika Nash, Larry Jointer, Ali Muhammed, Jacquetta Beane-Haggens, Janice Walker, Dranda Jones, Jennifer Greene, Burcey Hines, Janet Mckinney, Rosemary Wilson, Desiree Kemp, Stephanie Sudersky, Phelida Hughes, Kimyotta Thompson, Vanessa Roman, and Dr. Marchelle Lee

Pastor John Hannah of New Life Covenant Church and Dr. Stacey Spencer of New Direction Christian Church.

Lastly, Marilyn and Destined to Publish, thank you for making my dream a reality.

Aa

Annie the Alligator aspires to be a astronaut.

Bb

Bobby the Bear bounces the basketball with ease.

Cc

Carolyn the Camel cuddles next to her Mom for a cozy nap.

Dd

David the Dinosaur drives to the diner for donuts.

Ee

Elijah the Elephant enjoys peanuts for an evening snack.

Ff

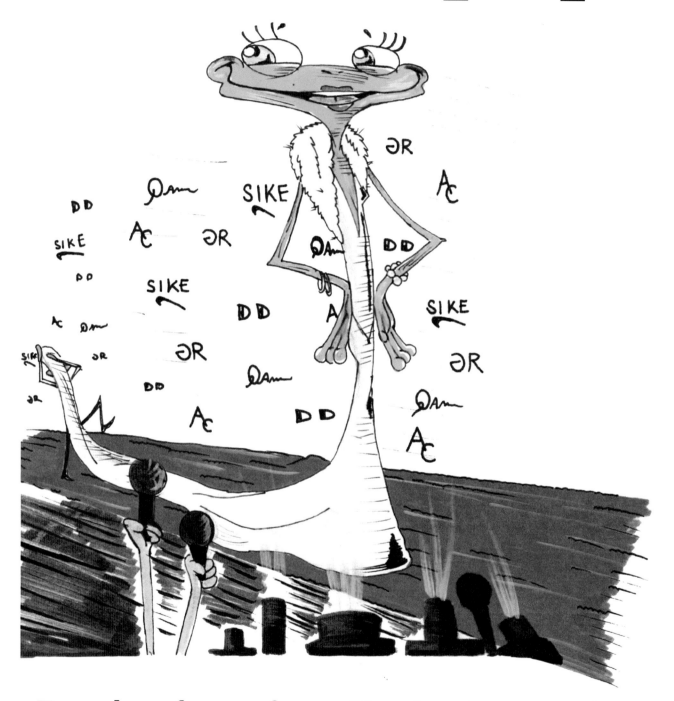

Fran is a fancy frog. She loves French fashion.

Gg

Granny Goose giggles at her grand-geese as they play a game.

Hh

Helen the Hippo hops with her hula hoops.

Isaiah the Iguana invites his friends to an ice cream social.

Jj

Joanne the Jaguar jumps for jellybeans in the Jamaican jamboree!

Kk

Kevin the Kangaroo lives in Kansas. He flies his kite on windy days.

Ll

Leah the Lioness loves flowers. Her favorites are lilies and lilacs.

Mm

Mino the Monkey makes moonpies with his mommy on Mondays.

Nn

Netta the Newt is a nice nurse. She serves her patients noodle soup.

Oo

Ollie the Orca occasionally makes a big splash in the ocean for fun.

Pp

Portia the Panda proudly paints purple pansies.

Qq

Quincy the quiet quail makes quality quilts.

Rr

Rose the Rabbit runs in a race. She is wearing her red ribbons for good luck.

Ss

Skippy the Super Seal stops a sailboat from sinking. Way to go, Skippy!

Tt

Teddy the Turtle is excited about his two front teeth. Say cheese, Teddy!

Uu

Ulysseus the Uguisu's uncle plays the ukulele.

Vv

Victor the Vulture is a volunteer. He plays video games with veterans at the hospital.

Ww

Willa the Walrus is a waitress at the Wal-fish Astoria Restaurant.

Xx

Xavier the Xiosaurus plays the xylophone at a concert in Xenia.

Yy

Yasmine the Yak yodels in Yosemite Park. Yodel-ay-hee-hoo!

Zz

Zoe the Zebra enjoys zesty zucchini at the zoo.

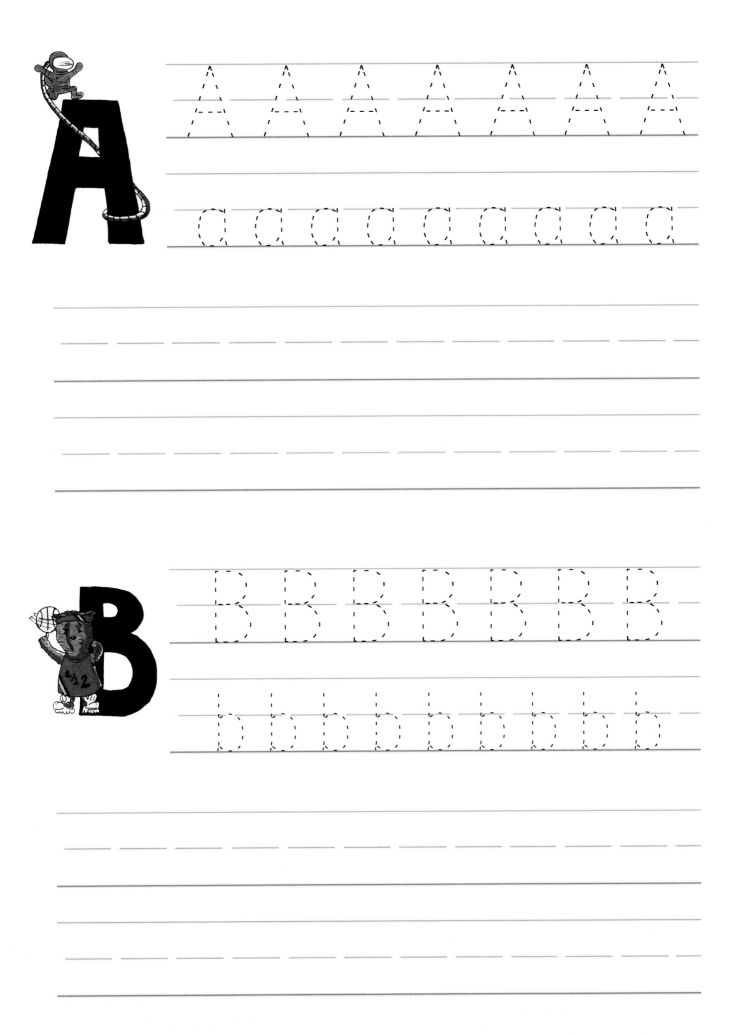

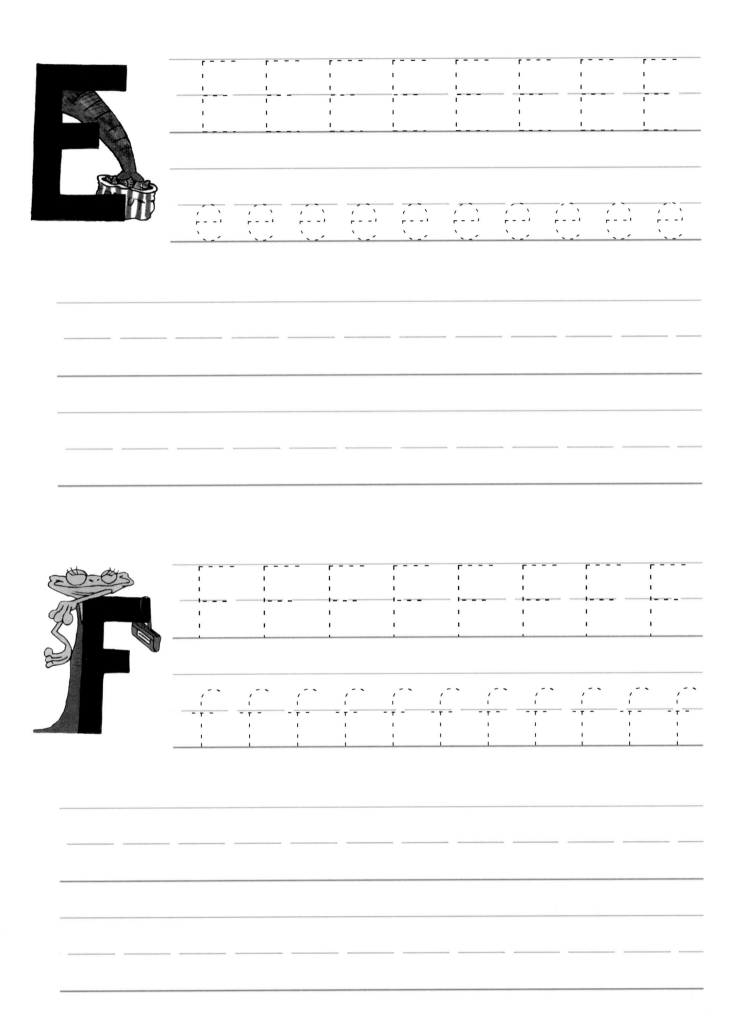

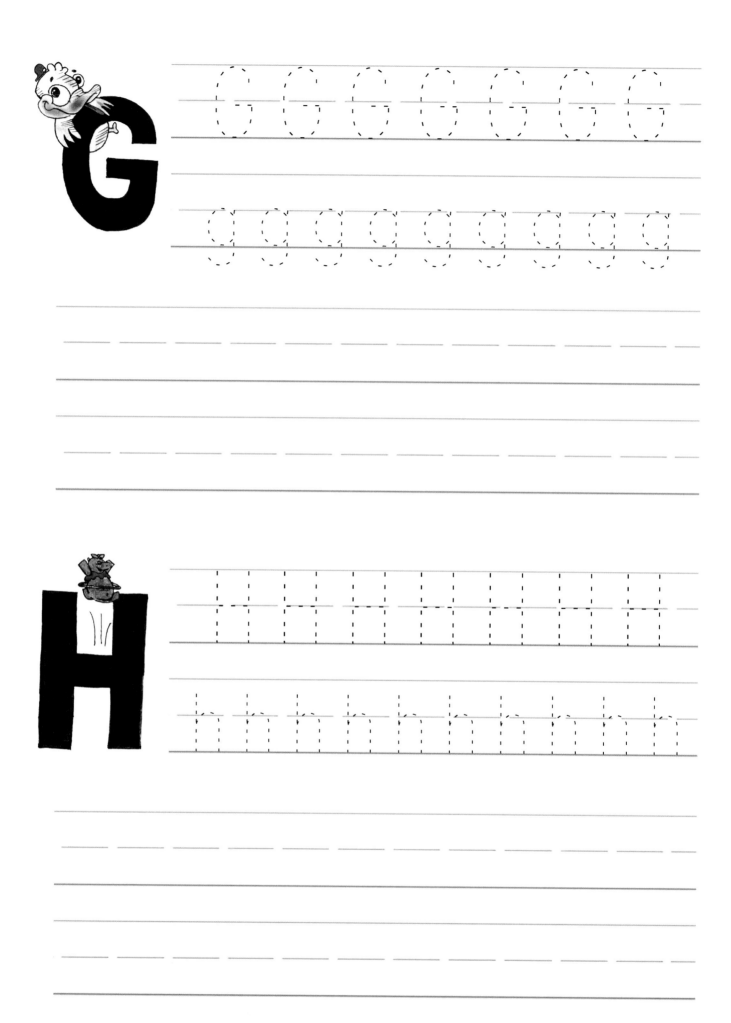

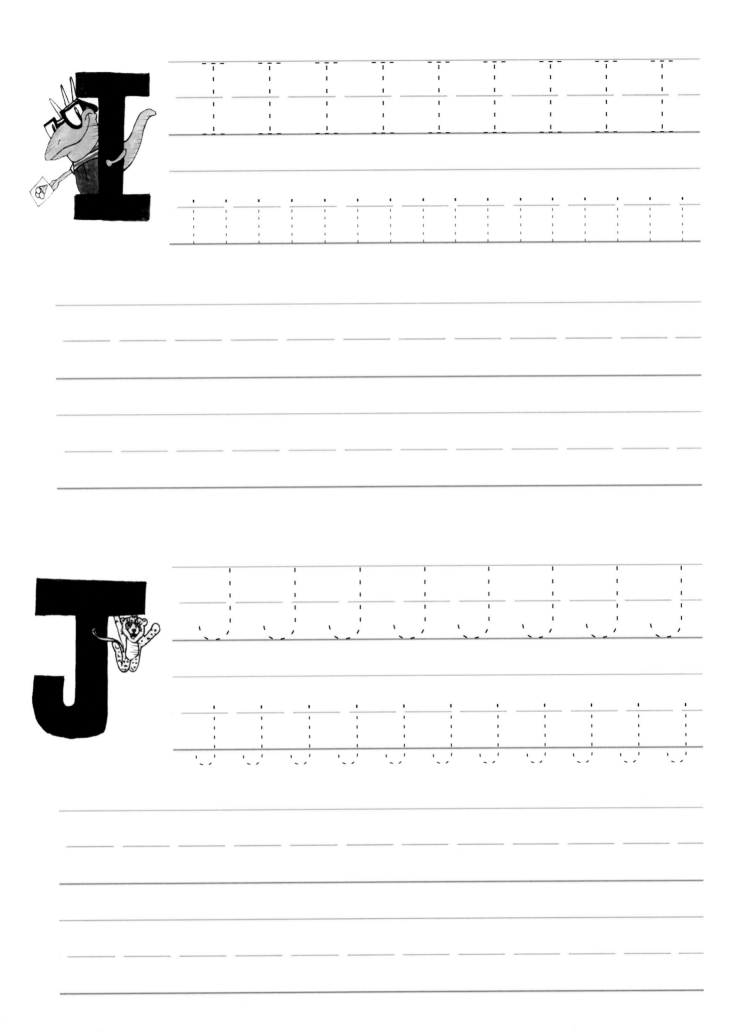

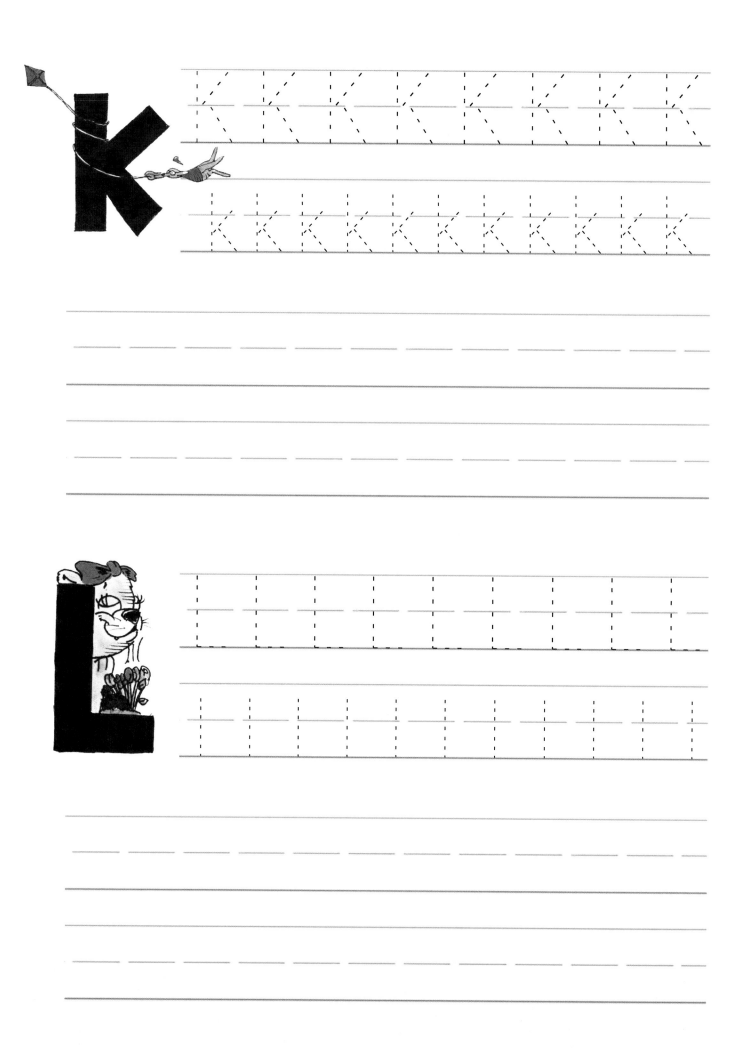

UN FACTS

A ....ALLIGATORS are apex predators that also eat fruit.

B ....The sun BEAR is the smallest bear in the world.

C ....CAMELS have three sets of eyelids and two rows of eyelashes to keep sand out of their eyes.

D ....DINOSAUR fossils have been found on all seven continents.

E ....The leader of a herd of ELEPHANTS is usually the oldest female—she is called the matriarch.

F ....FROGS don't need to drink water because they absorb it through their skin.

G ....GEESE can fly up to 40 miles per hour.

H ....When HIPPOS are upset, their sweat turns red.

I ....Green IGUANAS are excellent swimmers and will dive into the water to avoid predators.

J............The JAGUAR is the third largest of the big cats after the tiger and the lion; it is the largest of the big cats in the Americas.

K............On land, KANGAROOS usually hold their hind legs together. However, in water, they kick each leg independently to swim.

L............A LION'S roar can be heard up to five miles away.

M............A group of MONKEYS is called a troop or a barrel.

N............NEWTS have the ability to regenerate their limbs, eyes, spinal cords, hearts, intestines, and upper and lower jaws.

O............ORCAS are the most widespread mammals besides humans.

P............The PANDA spends 14–16 hours a day eating bamboo.

Q............QUAILS usually live alone, but they form flocks in the fall.

R............RABBITS are born with their eyes closed and without fur.

S ....A SEAL'S whiskers help it to detect prey in dark, murky waters.

T ....TURTLES don't have ears, but they are not deaf. Thin flaps of skin cover their inner ear; this allows them to sense vibrations and low-frequency sounds.

U ....An UGUISU is a small bird found in the Far East, particularly in Japan.

V ....VULTURES live in every part of the world except Australia and Antarctica.

W ....WALRUSES use their mighty tusks to forage for food and to lift themselves up onto sea ice.

X ....XIAOSAURUS was a small, lightly built dinosaur. It was a herbivore (plant-eater) and a swift runner. It was lizard-like and about 5 feet long.

Y ....Wild male YAKS can reach a height of 6-and-a-half feet and can weigh as much as 2,200 pounds.

Z ....A baby ZEBRA can run an hour after it is born.

Helen L. Robinson is a seasoned educator and lover of children's literature who is passionate about reading.

For over twenty years, Helen has inspired young minds as a kindergarten teacher, early interventionist, special-education assistant, and mentor. She earned a Bachelor of Science in Education at Rust College in Holly Springs, Mississippi, in 1997.

She has worked for the Cleveland Municipal School District, Prince William County School District, and the Chicago Public School District, and currently works for Shelby County School District in Memphis, Tennessee.

Helen has three children and resides in Mississippi; this is her first publication.

Made in the USA
Monee, IL
18 May 2021